The Ice Age in the Lake District

Alan Smith

'THE COMING OF THE ICE'

"It has been said that when God made England his finger touched but did not press, but that is not true of Cumberland and Westmorland. He pressed there all right. What is more he used his nails. And his nails were ice".

NORMAN NICHOLSON
Portrait of the Lakes 1963

INTRODUCTION

Most of us are familiar with the phrase 'The Ice Age'. It conjures up a picture of great ice sheets and glaciers covering the landscape, a time of perpetual winter and of harsh conditions inhospitable to life.

This booklet attempts to explain what ice-age conditions were like in the Lake District. Although the framework of the district is written in its geology with the rocks controlling the major outlines, it was the work of ice and cold climate processes during what we rather simply call 'The Ice Age' that fashioned the present day appearance of our district and left the fells and dales looking the way they do.

The booklet will try to illustrate in simple terms how we can show that ice and glaciers once existed. We experienced not just one Ice Age but several. For the last 2.6 million years of geological time the climate has swung back and forth between periods of relative warmth and very severe full glacial situations - a cycle we are still in today. How cold was it in the Lake District? How much ice did we have? When did the glaciers and ice sheets build up and melt away? Do we have any evidence of life during these ice-age times? All are relevant questions. Evidence to help us piece together this jigsaw of ice-age times is out there in the Lakeland landscape of today.

Back in Victorian times, little more than 150 years ago, people needed convincing that ice ever existed in the Lake District. The notion that the Lakeland valleys had been carved out by glaciers, that the lake basins had been scoured out by moving ice, or that the thick layers of clay and boulders spread over the valley floors and lowlands had been brought there by ice sheets could not be comprehended. Most people had never seen a glacier or ice-sheet. How could ice sheets exert such crushing forces? Ice-ages had no obvious causes. On the other hand, the Great Biblical Flood did have some credibility in some peoples' minds. Gradually, as people began to travel, as geologists and scientists began to observe and study the earth, the evidence for changing climates and ice age conditions in the past was demonstrated. Most recently, the application of scientific research to contemporary polar and high-mountain ice caps and glaciers and to the record preserved in the sediments on the floors of the oceans has begun to shed light on this period and help us understand what recent ice-age events were like.

THE TIMESCALE

Scientists are now able to give us quite a good picture of how our climate has been changing over the recent past. By coring the ocean floor sediments, coring the Greenland and Antarctic ice caps, measuring and monitoring the behaviour of modern glaciers and ice sheets, and by detailed analysis of recent fossil remains it can be demonstrated that over the last 2.6 million years we have had several periods of particularly cold conditions. Progressively the record is becoming clearer and we are able to put more accurate details and more precise dates on events.

Figure 1 shows in very simple terms how the climate of Northern Britain has rapidly swung back and forth between periods of extreme cold and relative warmth. It is immediately apparent the term 'The Ice Age' is a misnomer – we are not dealing with just one big freeze but many. We have had periods we can rightly call **glacials** (or ice ages) when ice sheet conditions and severe temperatures were the norm, but also periods between, which we call **interglacials**, when conditions were more temperate and relatively warm. A glance at the top of the graph, which refers to the present, shows we are merely in an interglacial at the moment – a period of relative warmth.

Geologists have demonstrated that around 2.6 million years ago there was a distinct change in climate over the Northern Hemisphere. A line has thus been drawn here in the earth's timescale – this period (extremely short in geological terms) we now know as the **Quaternary** (the fourth era). Apart from this being a time of quickly oscillating temperatures, the graph shows us two other important points. First, that taking the long view, climatic conditions seem to be worsening – severe cold spells are more a feature of the very recent past (the last 1 million years), whereas before that the warm spells were longer. Secondly, there appears to be a regularity in this swing between cold and warm - a regular cycle (we will return to this later).

All these cold phases **(glacials)** shown in Figure 1 have been given names, similarly the **interglacials** between them. The important point however, is that our knowledge and understanding rapidly diminishes as we go back down this timescale. As far as the Lake District is concerned most of the features we can look at, or the deposits that have been left for us to examine relate to the very last glacial phase **(The Last Glacial Maximum, LGM or Devensian Glacial)**. We have some knowledge of the interglacial that preceded it but fairly sparse evidence of the glacial before that. Earlier events we can only speculate about. The effect of glacial conditions in the Lake District was primarily erosive and destructive. Each ice sheet wiped away the evidence of the one before it. The landscape is therefore rather like a white board, written on is the last activity, previous records have been largely wiped clean but just in a few places it is still possible to vaguely discern the earlier text.

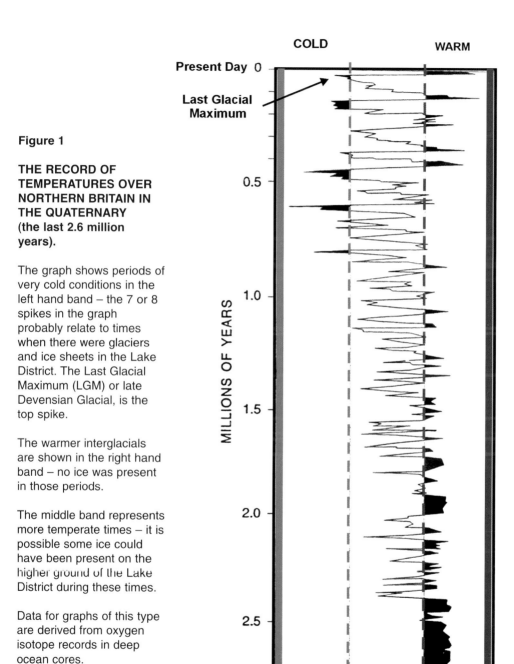

Figure 1

THE RECORD OF TEMPERATURES OVER NORTHERN BRITAIN IN THE QUATERNARY (the last 2.6 million years).

The graph shows periods of very cold conditions in the left hand band – the 7 or 8 spikes in the graph probably relate to times when there were glaciers and ice sheets in the Lake District. The Last Glacial Maximum (LGM) or late Devensian Glacial, is the top spike.

The warmer interglacials are shown in the right hand band – no ice was present in those periods.

The middle band represents more temperate times – it is possible some ice could have been present on the higher ground of the Lake District during these times.

Data for graphs of this type are derived from oxygen isotope records in deep ocean cores.

THE ORIGIN OF ICE AGES

Glaciers and ice sheets build up in a very simple way. Snowfall collects on the surface of the ground. As more and more from later falls is added, the mass compacts and is progressively transformed under its own weight into ice. Eventually it will flow and deform as it is pulled by gravity. As long as temperatures are low enough to prevent complete melting, the balance will be in favour of accumulation. There are no glaciers in the Lake District at present simply because the snow that falls on the fells each winter melts away in the following spring and early summer, so every winter the process starts again with no carry over from the preceding one. Cooler summers and not unduly harsher winters could easily tip the balance. The higher the fells the more likely they are to collect snow and obviously our latitudinal position is also important. If we did start moving into a cooler spell, Scotland, for example, with higher mountains and a more northerly position would see glaciers building up sooner than here in the Lake District. More local conditions are also important in understanding how and where a glacier will originate. Snow accumulation will be related to the pattern of precipitation which may for example reflect such factors as the local relief and the direction of prevailing winds. There is evidence that the W and SW Lake District had larger and more active glaciers than areas further east where there were rain shadow effects.

A much more fundamental question is why has our climate been changing, why has it been swinging back and forth in an apparently regular pattern between cold glacials and milder interglacials. Scientists have been speculating on these problems for a long time. All sorts of theories have been proposed. The theory that at present has found the most acceptance is the so called 'astronomical theory' which basically shows that the earth surface temperatures are controlled by variations in the earths orbit of the sun. These variations are regular and predictable and can be quantified. The ideas were first propounded by a Scottish scientist James Croll in the 1860s. However it was a rather obscure Serbian mathematician, Milutin Milankovitch who spent over 30 years perfecting it, publishing the results of his laborious manual calculations in the 1930s and 40s. For many years his ideas lay dormant and unadopted. Over the last 30 years or so, however, it has come to be recognised that Milankovitch was probably right and these cycles are the main factors behind climatic oscillations.

Three cycles operate on different timescales. The cycle of **eccentricity** relates to the fact that the earth's orbit changes from being less elliptical to more elliptical about every 100,000 years. Secondly, **obliquity**, that is the fact that the axis of the earth varies in inclination over time with a regular cycle lasting 41,000 years. Thirdly the **precession**, which, put very simply, is that the earth wobbles slightly with a cycle lasting 23,000 years. These three cycles combine to cause regular changes in the level of sunlight falling on the earth. Polar ice caps expand and contract in response to these 'Milankovitch Cycles'.

These cyclical events do not explain all the observed oscillations. Many other factors are also involved such as the disposition of the continents, in particular the presence of land masses over the poles, variations in ocean circulation and sea levels, uplift of mountain ranges and the composition of the atmosphere.

If this pattern of climatic oscillation that we have experienced for the last 2.6 million years continues, we are clearly heading for another very cold spell. The present interglacial has already lasted over 10,000 years, the cyclical pattern of the past shows interglacials average only about 8,000 years and rarely last up to 15,000 years. The next glacial therefore is already probably not very far off. Glacials last for something like 100,000 years when they occur. 90% of the last 750,000 years has seen glacial conditions.

How all this fits with current threats over global warming presents, to say the least, an interesting question. Current warming trends may well be outweighed by the factors driving the long term pattern. We may have to wait until the pattern of continents and oceans on the earth are no longer as they are now before things change. On the other hand, as we will see when we look at glacial events a little more closely from evidence here in the Lake District, climatic change can be quite sudden. It takes relatively little change to plunge us back into a situation where ice could start accumulating again on the fells and we are into a rapid downward spiral.

THE LAST GLACIAL

It is possible to reconstruct a reasonably good picture of the last glacial period in the Lake District. The imprint of this is still fresh in the landscape. Figure 1 took the long view of climatic change over the last 2.6 million years and illustrated the constant oscillation between the cold **glacials** and the intervening milder phases (**interglacials**). There could have been as many as 21 distinct **glacials** over this period but it is the very last one (the **DEVENSIAN**) and the time immediately before and after, that we must now focus on.

Figure 2 provides a picture of approximate temperature fluctuations over the last 130,000 years. Immediately before the Lake District plunged into the last **Devensian** glacial there was a short interglacial known as the **Ipswichian** and before that a glacial known as the **Wolstonian**.

We have only a few scraps of evidence of these earlier phases in the Lake District. The **WOLSTONIAN** lasted from approximately 160,000 years ago until 128,000 years ago. Ice existed in the Lake District and as Figure 4 shows covered most of the British Isles except for the extreme south of England. Some recent boreholes drilled by Nirex in the 1990s for the investigations into possible deep nuclear waste storage facilities near the Sellafield site in West Cumbria passed through a series of clays and glacial debris which experts dated to this period. There is also a site in Mosedale Beck, Threlkeld, near Keswick where some glacial clays probably date from this period too, but they need specialist expertise to recognise.

The **IPSWICHIAN** interglacial began approximately 128,000 years ago. The climate, being milder, allowed the growth of vegetation and some animal life existed. Their remains, now usually preserved in peat deposits, can be dated. The Lake District however, is not a good area to find such remains, these deposits are better preserved in lowland areas of Britain – the chronology of the **Ipswichian**, and obviously its name, is derived from locations in East Anglia. However, in 1978 local scientists did get quite excited by the discovery of some wood remains and peat in a river bank at Scandale Beck in the Upper Eden valley in Cumbria which was dated to this phase. The site is now preserved and has SSSI protection, but such locations are rare in Lakeland and do not excite the uninformed eye.

Initial cooling of our climate and the plunge into the last glacial (the **DEVENSIAN**) started around 118,000 years ago. As the climate curve in Figure 2 shows, temperatures were still fluctuating and there was no immediate drop into severe glacial conditions. In fact the first few thousand years of the Devensian in the Lake District may not have seen the accumulation of much ice, the climate may have been cold but relatively dry. Progressively however, average temperatures over the whole of the Northern Hemisphere dropped and patterns of precipitation changed, ice built up and intense glacial conditions prevailed.

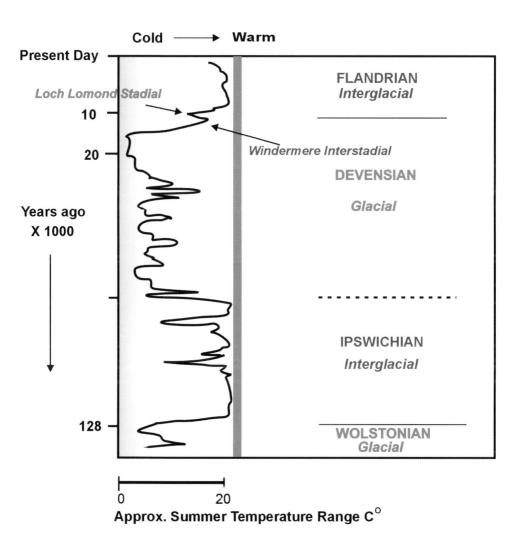

Figure 2 Temperature change over the last 130,000 years.

Figure 3 shows the extent of ice over Northern Europe at the Devensian maximum which was reached around 18,000 years ago. Ice covered most of the British Isles, except for southern England, and extended from Scandinavia south into Germany and S. Russia. Smaller ice caps extended from the Alps (A) and the Pyrenees (P).

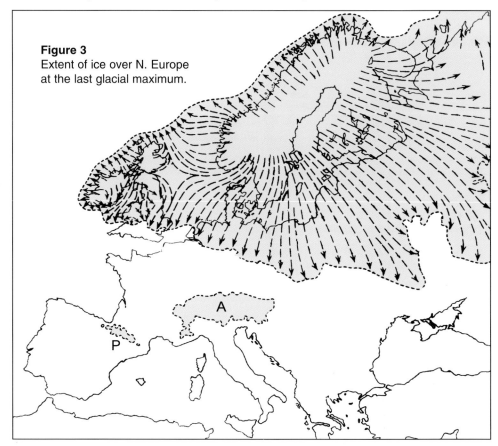

Figure 3
Extent of ice over N. Europe at the last glacial maximum.

Over the British Isles (Figure 4) ice built up particularly over the mountains of Scotland, but Lakeland was also high enough and cold enough to generate its own ice cap, as were the mountains of Wales and parts of Ireland. Starting from small accumulations over the high fells and in sheltered and shaded high valleys ice progressively covered most of the landscape coalescing with ice from Scotland and neighbouring parts of Northern England. Ice moved out radially from the Lake District, northwards and westwards into the Solway Basin where it was diverted south by Scottish ice, and south-westwards and southwards into the Irish Sea where it streamed down into Lancashire and Cheshire. On the eastern side ice moved through the Tyne gap into Northumbria and over Stainmore across the Pennines into N.Yorkshire. The detailed patterns of flow can be detected from the landforms left behind as the ice scraped and scratched its way over rock surfaces and by trails of debris (**erratics**) picked up by the ice and later abandoned far from their original source. Boulders of Shap Granite for example can be traced across Stainmore and into the Vale of York and erratics of Criffel Granites from Dumfries are spread over N. Cumbria and along the W.Cumbria and Furness coasts. Once ice flow over the landscape had been established, patterns and directions were constantly changing, in some places ice was active and highly mobile, in others it was static and restricted in its impact. Over time the ice waxed and waned, thickening and thinning as conditions oscillated, changing as climatic conditions allowed.

There is still debate about how far the Devensian ice sheet extended, particularly southwards in the Irish Sea for example. Its limits on land are clearer (Figure 4). Lakeland ice clearly penetrated well down into Cheshire and the NW Midlands as well as over into the North East of England and into the Vale of York. Along the Cumbrian coastal strip and in Furness the picture is often one of Scottish and local Lakeland ice competing; at times Scottish ice moving on to what is now the Cumbria coast, at others Lakeland ice being able to move out south-westward and join the Irish Sea icestream.

The Devensian ice sheet reached its maximum extent round about 18,000 years ago. The evidence suggests that the ice cap over Lakeland really started to grow only from about 30,000 years ago and lasted for a relatively short time. We know from the sediments left on the floors of the major lakes that it had all melted away by 13,500 years ago and we were back into a short interglacial (**The Windermere Interstadial**). This was followed by a further minor set back in climatic conditions. We plunged back into a mini-glacial for no more than a 1000 years (**The Loch Lomond Readvance**). Since then, the last 10,000 years or so up to the present day (**The Flandrian**), we have been experiencing what in geological terms have been interglacial milder conditions. We will return to these more recent events in a later section.

DATING ICE AGE EVENTS: Putting precise dates on ice age events such as the beginning and ends of the various glacials and interglacials is an extremely specialised and complex procedure. A range of scientific techniques are in use to date material, each requiring a high level of scientific understanding. Dates given in the published literature are frequently not fully explained and hence there can be confusion in understanding actual dates. Some types of dating methods (for example radiocarbon dating) can only be used over limited parts of the timescale. Others such as thermoluminescence (TL) and amino-acid methods are only reliable when applied to specific materials. Dating is also done by other types of isotopic methods, dendrochronology (tree rings) and cosmogenic data.

Radiocarbon dates (the dominant source) do not equate with calendar years. Carbon 14 dates are usually expressed as 14C years before present (BP) where 'present' is, by convention, the standard year 1950 AD. Increasingly it has become the practice to calibrate 14C years to actual calendar years – these are usually written as cal BP. Calibration is a very complex correction process.

In this booklet for ease of understanding I have used 14C years for more recent dates (Devensian and later). For example the Loch Lomond Readvance (Stadial) is shown as 11-10kaBP (ie 11,000 -10,000 years before 1950). In fact when calibrated this stadial comes out at 12.9-11.5 cal BP. Older timelines are shown calibrated or follow conventional geological dating by radiometric methods.

THE LAKELAND ICE CAP

Many attempts have been made to model what the ice cap over the Lake District looked like in the Devensian and to estimate how thick it was and how it was moving. The evidence from the landscape does not give us conclusive answers. Modern computer modelling based on climatic predictions is also open to debate and there have been several conflicting hypotheses put forward in the scientific literature.

Although the Devensian ice only existed for less than 20,000 years, there must have been variations in its thickness within that time. Most models reconstruct a rounded ice dome feature covering the Lake District fells, sloping down in all directions and moving radially outwards from the central fells. At the maximum (18,000 years ago) it has been suggested it was as high as 1600m, ie some 600m above the highest fell tops. At the same time, ice over the Scottish Highlands perhaps stood higher at 1800m. Calculations of surface temperature conditions at the maximum range as low as -18°C, with basal temperatures beneath the ice of between -6°C and -4°C. At such extremes the ice could not have been very active being essentially frozen to the ground and accomplishing little erosion. More temperate conditions however, must have prevailed for much of the time, as it is clear that ice was actively moving across many of the fell tops scratching, scouring and eroding the surface and streams of rapid ice flow were active along the major valley lines.

The major lake basins, which are noticeably disposed in a radial pattern and were clearly gouged out by ice, are strong evidence of the power of this outward moving flow controlled by the gradient of the ice surface. There is also strong evidence that ice movement may have been more active over much of western and south-western Lakeland where ice may have had easier egress off the ice dome and may also have had higher levels of precipitation feeding the glaciers. Ice had relatively free egress down the valleys of western and south western Lakeland, the ice streams coalescing with Irish Sea ice moving southwards. To the north and east, Lakeland ice was more congested having to join the flow northwards down the Eden valley and round westwards into the Solway, or take routes eastwards over the Pennine watershed. Scottish ice moving southwards appears to have been deflected around the northern Lake District, inferred by the lowland landforms of the Solway which are all of Lakeland provenance and the lack of Scottish erratics within the mountainous parts of Lakeland. Scottish ice did however impinge on to the South Cumbrian coast at a later stage.

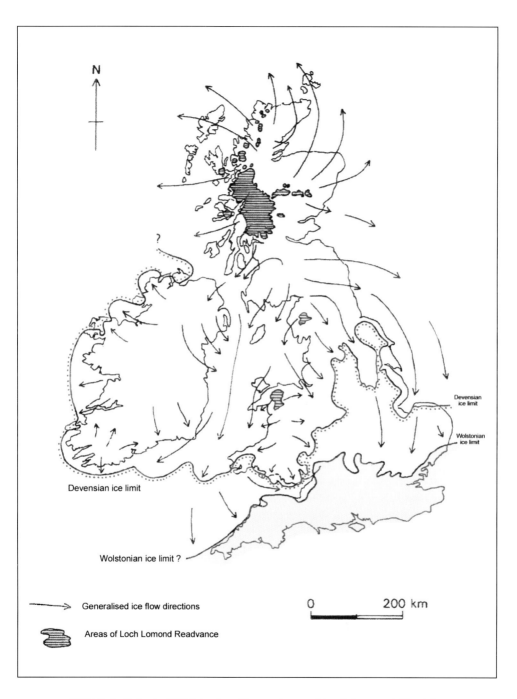

Figure 4 Extent of Wolstonian, Devensian and Loch Lomond Glacials.

13

DETECTING ICE MOVEMENTS

Ice as it passes over the landscape scratches, smoothes and moulds rock surfaces and moves rock material from one place to another. Painstaking recording and measurement of often quite small features has made it possible to deduce the directions of ice movement and work out the disposition of the main ice flows over the Lakeland region.

STRIATIONS:

Striations are small, shallow grooves that have been scratched into rock surfaces over which a glacier has passed. The ice itself does not cause such abrasions but the projections of the rock debris held rigidly in basal ice act as the cutting tools. Striations are usually not more than a few millimetres in depth and only a few centimetres long. They are best preserved in hard resistant rocks – particularly the volcanic rocks of central Lakeland. Their interpretation needs care. Single scratches are weak evidence of ice movement, multiple marks and grooves showing a consistent orientation are stronger indicators. Frequently however they may merely suggest the orientation of the ice flow, but not its direction. This may only be revealed by other corroborating evidence. Cross cutting striations are sometimes found and are useful in indicating two separate sets of ice movement over a surface at different times.

Figure 5 STRIATIONS ON A SLATE SURFACE. The direction of ice movement is from left to right. The clearest striations are just below the 50p coin.

STREAMLINED BEDROCK FEATURES:

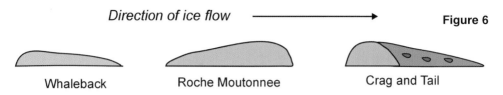

Direction of ice flow ⟶ **Figure 6**

Whaleback Roche Moutonnee Crag and Tail

A common effect of ice passing over a landscape is the streamlining of bedrock protrusions into **whaleback** or elongated, rounded ridge features aligned with the direction of ice flow. Figure 7 below shows a long narrow whaleback feature near Puddingstone Bank in the Watendlath valley. The ice was moving from bottom right to left in the picture.

Figure 7

Slightly different features can be produced where ice is thin and moving quickly. Low pressures within the ice allow cavities to open up. Under such conditions bedrock hills and small knolls are shaped into **Roches Moutonnees** (literally sheep rocks, because they resemble sheep lying down). They are much larger features than sheep however, usually several metres in length but they can be tens or hundreds of metres. They are common along the floors of the glacial troughs of the main Lakeland valleys. The up-sides (**stoss**) of these features experience glacial abrasion, striation and smoothing. On the down–sides (**lee**) where cavities in the ice can open up and water pressures under the ice can vary, glacial plucking occurs; blocks of rock are pulled away and carried from the face of the protrusion.

Figure 8
A roche moutonnee shaped in the volcanic rock of Yewdale, Coniston, in South Lakeland. The ice was moving from right to left (N to S). Smoothed and striated surfaces on the gentle stoss side to the right, steep plucked rock face to the left (lee).

CRAG AND TAIL:

Ice moving over a rocky crag which proves too resistant to erode away, will sometimes leave a tail of glacial debris (clay, cobbles, boulders) streamlined out on the lee side of the obstruction. This becomes a **crag and tail**. Castlehead, a resistant plug of quartz-diorite rock standing up in the landscape, to the south of Keswick, close to the shore of Derwentwater is an excellent example. A tail of glacial till extends for about 500m north westwards behind the crag, which protrudes about 70m above the surrounding area.

Figure 9
A train of rounded Shap Granite erratics strewn across the Westmorland limestone plateau near Hardendale. The ice was moving in the direction of the view.

ERRATICS AND ERRATIC TRAINS:

Pebbles and boulders picked up by ice and transported some distance from their source yield information about the direction of ice movement and are termed **erratics**. Boulders of distinctive rocks like Shap Granite for example, have been traced across the North Pennines far into Yorkshire, or down onto the Lancashire Plain and into Cheshire. Similarly Scottish rocks were carried by ice across to Cumbria. To be good indicators erratics have to be of rock types resistant enough to withstand transport and distinctive enough to pinpoint their sources.

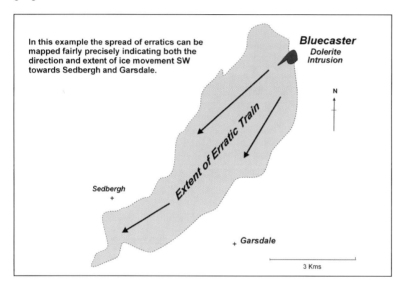

In this example the spread of erratics can be mapped fairly precisely indicating both the direction and extent of ice movement SW towards Sedbergh and Garsdale.

Bluecaster
Dolerite Intrusion

N

Extent of Erratic Train

Sedbergh +

+ Garsdale

3 Kms

Figure 10
Erratic Train
from the
Bluecaster
Dolerite
Intrusion
in the Rawthey
Valley, in SE
Lakeland.

Criffel

Figure 11
Large erratics
of Granite
stranded on
the North
Cumbria coast
near Allonby –
transported by
ice from Criffel
25kms away
on the Scottish
side of the
Solway Firth.

THE HIGH FELL TOPS

Many of the questions posed already about the possible thickness of ice cover over the Lakeland fell tops at the last Glacial Maximum and whether the ice was moving and eroding or was possibly just lying inactive, should be able to be answered by looking at the present day form of this high landscape. Interestingly the evidence on the ground is tantalisingly inconclusive.

Most fellwanderers will be well aware that much of the high ground over the western and south-western fells is rough and rugged terrain with strong evidence that this is a landscape severely scoured and scraped across by ice. Much of it is reminiscent of what over NW Scotland is described as 'knock and lochan topography'. Areas of highly irregular, often chaotic relief, rough ice shorn outcrops of rocky crags (knocks) separated by depressions with pools and small tarns (lochans) or accumulations of peat and upland bogs. Examination of the rocky outcrops reveals striations, ice smoothing and moulding of the relief into ridge forms reflecting the direction of ice movement. Good examples of this type of terrain are the summits of Hard Knott, Eskdale Fell, Harter Fell, Haystacks, the Seathwaite Fells or the Dunnerdale Fells (Figure 12 and Back Cover).

Figure 12 Ice scoured terrain, Dawson Ground Crags, Eskdale Fells.

In contrast to these rugged fell tops in the west what are we to make of the summit of the Helvellyn and High Street ridges in eastern Lakeland? There, the summit areas are smooth, flat or gently undulating with absolutely no evidence of ice having moved across them (Figure 13). There is no roughened ground and no trace of glacial erratics. Glaciers have certainly bitten into their flanks excavating great cirque amphitheatres almost like pastry cutters on a biscuit board, but the summits appear untouched. It has been suggested they may even be ancient surfaces worn down by erosion in the Tertiary period of geological time (more than 10 million years ago), long before the ice came on to the scene at all. The smoothness and evenness of the Helvellyn summit is borne out by the fact that an aeroplane was landed on the summit in December 1926, admittedly in a madcap escapade by two early aerial pioneers. There is a memorial commemorating the event on the summit today. Without doubt however we have to conclude that the impact of ice on these eastern summits has been minimal.

Figure 13 The summit plateau of Helvellyn.

Some very recent research has presented some new ideas on the nature of the Lakeland high summits. It has been suggested that the very highest summit areas of the Central fells (Scafell/Scafell Pike, Pillar, Great Gable, Esk Pike and Bowfell) actually poked through the Devensian ice cap as exposed peaks (**nunataks**), (Figure 14).

Three lines of evidence have been advanced in support of this. First, these summit areas show large areas of frost shattered rock outcrops, with deeply opened joints in the rock surfaces, and spreads of boulders and angular **blockfields** similar to frost shattered summit areas in high mountains or of exposed rock in polar latitudes today (Figure 15).

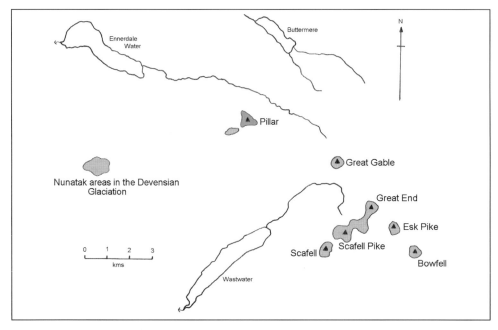

Figure 14 Nunatak areas in the Devensian Glaciation.

Figure 15 Frost shattered blockfield on the summit of Broad Crag.
View looking north from Scafell Pike.

20

The boundaries between this high level frost shattered terrain and areas of ice moulded and scraped ground beneath are often sharp.

Second, there is evidence of 'trimlines', that is steepening of the flanks of these summit areas where the edges of the ice cut into and scraped around the edges of the nunataks (Figure 16). This interpretation implies that the ice sheet reached a maximum altitude of only c. 870m around Bow Fell in the east, declining to 830-850m around the Scafell Pike massif and to 800-830m around Pillar in the NW.

Figure 16 Trimlines on the flanks of Great Gable.
View looking eastwards over Mirk Cove, from Scoat Fell.

Lastly complex chemical analysis of the broken down rock material and soils on these high summits above the trimlines shows high percentages of certain clay minerals (albite and gibbsite) which are known to be representative of chemical decomposition under severe frost conditions.

This work is clearly at odds with theoretical models that suggested the ice dome over the Lake District stood as high as 1600m. Other models have put the upper limits much lower, some in the region of 900m. Debate on these issues still goes on in the scientific world.

ICE IN THE VALLEYS

The main radiating Lakeland valleys acted as the routeways for ice to discharge outwards from the district. There may have been times in the Devensian when the ice dome covered the fells completely. There were also times when the highest summits poked through the ice and perhaps summit plateaux in the east had just thin covers of ice and snow protecting them. Nevertheless the valleys were always the principal conduits for the flowing ice. Ice used and modified the existing valleys, steepening and scouring their sides, deepening their floors and in places straightening their alignment sometimes cutting across ridges and cols creating new routes.

Classic glaciated valleys are often referred to as **troughs** (a good description of their form), or rather more simplistically as being U shaped. In reality if we look at the major Lakeland valleys such as Borrowdale, Langdale, Ennerdale or Wasdale their sides are far from vertical as in the letter U. Compared with the classic ice carved valleys of say Yosemite in the Sierra Nevada of California or Lauterbrunnen in the Swiss Alps where vertical rock walls are seen, the Lakeland troughs are on a much more restrained scale. The Lakeland valleys have been shaped by repeated phases of river erosion and successive phases of glaciation, the last ice in the Devensian was just the latest phase of deepening and sharpening.

The excavation of glacial troughs and the creation of lake basins in their floors are largely due to glaciers quarrying joint-bounded blocks of rock from their beds. This is a two stage process. Blocks must be loosened by easing joints open or propagating new cracks. Ice must then exert traction on the loosened blocks and carry them forward. Water at the base of glaciers enhances sliding of the ice over the bedrock. This can lead to rapid fluctuations in water pressure and differences in pressure between rock cavities and cracks. This appears to lead to propagation of cracks in bedrock, particularly in rocks of low permeability like the hard, massive volcanic rocks of central Lakeland. Increasing water pressure increases sliding and reduces frictional resistance to dislodging blocks. In this way large pieces of rock are **plucked** from the valley floor, incorporated into the basal ice, moved forward to rub over and abrade rock lower down leaving **striations**.

Rock type is thus important in explaining the detailed form of the troughs of Lakeland (Compare Figures 17, 18 & 19). Most of central Lakeland, where nearly all the major valleys originate, is formed of strongly jointed, blocky volcanic rocks of the Borrowdale Volcanic Group. These are hard volcanic lavas, thick resistant beds of tuff (volcanic ash) and thick sequences of other types of debris created in violent volcanic explosions. These rocks were heavily plucked by the glaciers but their massive, blocky, craggy nature prevailed in the landscape. Valley sides are therefore rugged and rocky; steep crags and prominent bastions of rock rim these valleys and irregular knolls and striated knobs of rocks remain where the ice overrode them. Over the northern and north-western fells however, ice was eroding different rocks - the grey mudstones, siltstones and slatey rocks we know as the Skiddaw

Figure 17 STONETHWAITE VALLEY, Borrowdale, view looking up the valley from near Longthwaite. A broad, flat floored glacial trough in Borrowdale Volcanic Group rocks. Ice steepened, rough, rocky valley sides with flat infilled valley floor.

Figure 18 SAIL BECK VALLEY N.W. Fells, view looking up the valley. A glaciated valley in Skiddaw Group rocks. Note the open V shaped cross profile. Smooth, straight or, gently concave valley side slopes with few free rock faces.

Group. These responded differently to the passage of ice. Steep rocky crags are fewer here. The rocks break down more easily and produce finer debris; consequently valley sides are smoother and closer to a V shape. Much loose fine rock debris still blankets valley side slopes and extends across valley floors (Figure 19).

Figure 19 The Buttermere Glacial Trough. The view is from the summit of Mellbreak looking up the valley. The steep sided troughs at the head of the valley are cut into Borrowdale Volcanic rocks. To the right (south side) the rugged slopes are formed of the Ennerdale Granite. The opposite (north side) are on Skiddaw Group rocks. The two lakes, Buttermere in the far distance and Crummock Water in the foreground occupy glacially excavated rock basins in the floor of the trough. Debris from the Skiddaw Group rocks on the south side has been washed into the trough and now forms the isthmus of land separating the two lakes.

Figure 20 shows the major ice flow directions at the height of the Devensian. Ice could move out easily from the westerly and southerly facing valleys, but once out onto the lower ground of west and south Cumbria it met southward moving Scottish and Irish Sea ice streams. The evidence of landforms and deposits along this western fringe indicates constant change in the positions of the two ice masses. On the other hand, ice in the north east (in the Ullswater and Haweswater valleys for example) seems to have been largely confined to the troughs for long periods with the ice moving relatively slowly, eventually joining the main Vale of Eden ice streams northwards and then westwards across the Solway plain. Ice in the upper Eden found escape routes eastwards across the Pennine watershed, notably at Stainmore. Within the central mountains the flow of ice across interfluves, perhaps over low cols occurred on a limited scale. Glacial **diffluence** as this is usually termed, can be demonstrated between Great and Little Langdale via the Blea Tarn col and from upper Borrowdale into the Newlands Valley via the Dalehead Tarn col. There is little evidence however of ice moving across the main east-west watershed across central Lakeland, either northwards or southwards.

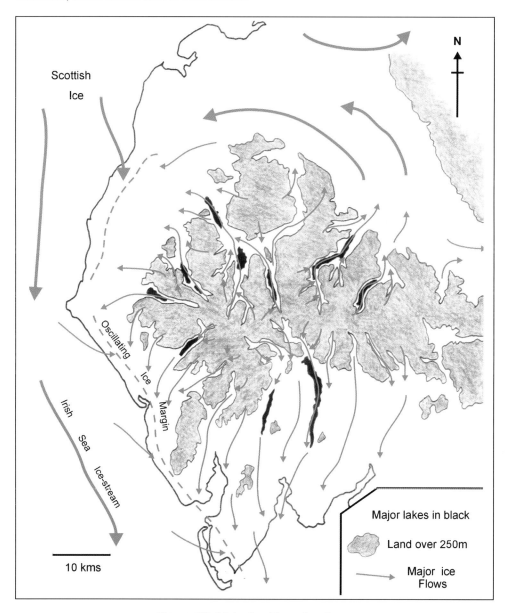

Figure 20 Major Ice Flow directions.

LAKES

As early as the mid 19th Century many writers, including the poet William Wordsworth, had commented upon the way the major lakes of the district radiate outwards like the spokes of a wheel from an imaginary point in the centre of the district. A circle of approximately 24 kms (15 miles) radius does in fact enclose all the major lake basins (Figure 21). It is the lake basins that emphasise the way ice moved out radially down the major glacial troughs in the Devensian glacial.

Figure 21

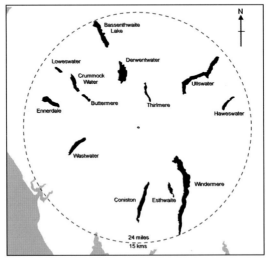

The pattern of ice flow in valley glaciers leads to uneven rates of erosion of the valley floors. In long profile the floors of glacial troughs typically become stepped; downward erosion becoming concentrated on the 'steps' (the level sections), whereas on the steeper 'risers', ice flow extends and accelerates, the rocks being overridden rather than being eroded. Small steps in valley profile which may originate from differences in rock type, or the confluence of two tributary valleys or perhaps from previous erosional events, thus become accentuated under glaciation. In this way erosive ice scooped out enclosed rock basins to create our major lakes, testimony to its power to remove hard rock and to flow over reversed gradients on the valley floors. Geologists call these deep, long, steep sided basins **Piedmont Lakes**, but the older less precise term **ribbon lakes** is more descriptive. Most of the lakes are single rock basins, but Windermere has two separately excavated basins and Ullswater three in its floor. The floor of Wastwater, the deepest of the basins is actually below sea level (see table). Much of the detailed form of the individual lakes is controlled by the local geology. The three separate basins in Ullswater and its dog-leg shape relates to the glacier cutting radially across the structural lines in the rocks. The width and shallowness of Derwentwater was the result of the glacier widening rather than deepening its valley in this section as it passed from volcanic rocks on to the less resistant Skiddaw Group rocks.

Looking closer and comparing the lake basins in the west and south west of the district with those in the east, illustrates differences in the effectiveness of ice as an eroding agent. Ice in the westerly and south westerly orientated valleys was able to move out directly into the Irish Sea Basin. All of the lakes in these valleys lie at relatively low altitudes as compared with lakes like Ullswater and Haweswater in the east. Wastwater, the deepest of all the lakes and others in the west (Ennerdale, Crummock Water and Buttermere) are relatively deep for their size (area). These facts support the view that glacial erosion was much more active in the west; glaciers were effective down to lower altitudes, had more temperate regimes and were probably moving more quickly. This is highly suggestive of higher snowfall in the west and south west of the district, mirroring the present day pattern of rainfall. In the rain shadowed eastern valleys glaciers whilst still being powerful erosive agents, were standing at higher levels.

Lake	Height above sea level in metres	Maximum depth in metres
Windermere	39.3	64.0
Esthwaite Water	65.4	15.5
Coniston Water	43.5	56.1
Wastwater	61.0	76.0
Ennerdale Water	112.3	42.0
Buttermere	101.0	28.6
Crummock Water	98.0	43.9
Loweswater	121.4	16.0
Bassenthwaite Lake	68.8	19.0
Derwentwater	74.5	22.0
Thirlmere *	179.1	46.0
Ullswater	145.0	62.5
Haweswater *	10.9	28.0

*original lakes

CIRQUES

Cirques are one of the most characteristic landforms of glacial erosion and one of the surest indicators of past glacial activity. Because of their broad distribution in glaciated mountains worldwide they often bear local names – for example **corrie** (or **coire**) in Scotland or **cwm** in Wales. In Lakeland they are often named **combs** (Gillercomb or Burtness Comb) or even **cove** (Nethermost Cove or Brown Cove).

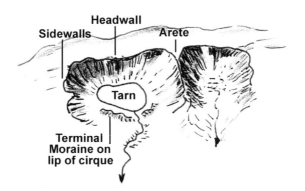

Figure 22
Cirque basins
with arête
between.

Cirques are basically arm-chair shaped hollows high up on mountain sides or at the head of glaciated troughs. They are open downstream but on the other three sides the hollow is rimmed by arcuate **sidewalls** and a steep (often rocky) **backwall** or **headwall**. The rounded floor of the cirque will often hold a small tarn and there is frequently a pronounced **lip** at the lower end formed of ice scoured bedrock and/or terminal moraine (Figure 22). Where two cirques meet, a precipitous sharp divide develops called an **arête**.

Cirques are the places where the glaciation of an upland area like the Lake District started and where it finally expired. Cirque initiation is quite complex, but in general, snow would accumulate first in high mountain recesses, steep valley heads and places where snowfall was high and could build up, protected by shade, from melting. In British mountains the optimum location for cirque development is in places with a northerly or north-easterly aspect. There, direct sunlight (**insolation**) is at a minimum and shade at a maximum – hence ice and snow persists for the longest. Equally important north-easterly facing slopes are in the lee of prevailing winds, which in British conditions are from the south-west. Snow accumulates faster on lee slopes. This is because snow is blown off high summit areas and carried into the lee of mountains where back eddying of the wind re-deposits the snow on the upper parts of the lee slope. The presence of a back eddy can often be seen in cirques by the way wavelets on cirque tarns move towards the back walls of the basin. The area of the summit plateau backing a cirque basin in a NE aspect is also significant, as potentially the greater the summit area the greater the amount of snow available to be blown on to the lee side (Figure 23).

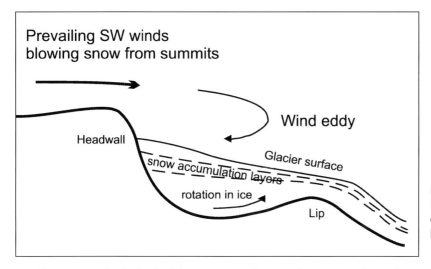

Figure 23 Features of a cirque basin.

Once a small glacier builds up in a valley head or recess it is able to deepen and exaggerate the hollow and create the rounded basin form of a cirque. Various processes are at work. Above the ice, the sidewalls and backwalls of the basin will be open to intense weathering by frost shattering. The key factor to understand however, is the way erosion beneath the ice can be concentrated at the base of the headwall, thus leading to excessive deepening at the back and bottom of the hollow and hence the creation of an enclosed rock basin. It has been shown by detailed examination of cirque glaciers today, in places like Norway, that the mass of ice rotates slightly. This was nicely illustrated by the fact that tunnels dug by scientists straight into cirque glaciers to examine what was happening to ice at the base of the backwall ceased to be horizontal over time, but progressively distorted and became downhill passages. Each year the amount of snow that builds up in cirques is greatest in the area high up on the glacier below the headwall. This is the area where snow blown from the summit plateau is concentrated and the greatest shade prevails. Further down glacier more melting occurs, particularly in summer. Each year therefore a wedge of fresh snow accumulates in the upper half of the glacier in winter and only partially melts in summer. This additional weight at the top drives the rotation. In the lower half of the glacier the flow will be upwards towards the surface (Figure 23). This encourages erosion of material from the floor of the basin. Rotation of the whole mass of ice maintains velocity of the ice over its bed. In this way an enclosed rock basin can be excavated by the ice pulling blocks of rock away from the basin floor and by grinding and abrading the bedrock. The ice will spill over the rock lip created at the lower end of the basin, scratching and striating the rock as it passes over. When deglaciation occurs the ice cover over the district thins away and the shaded cirque glacier may be the last refuge for ice in the region. Frost-riven debris from the headwalls and sidewalls of the cirque collecting on the ice surface and round its edges may build up on the cirque lip as a terminal moraine. As the ice eventually melts the basin fills with water and a tarn comes to occupy the cirque floor retained by the rock lip or in many cases in Lakeland made deeper by the arc of the terminal moraine.

The cirques on the High Street ridge in the east of the Lake District show all the classic features of these landforms and nicely illustrate why this area was favourable for cirque development (Figure 24 below). All the cirques lie on the eastern side of the ridge in the lee of the mountain mass. The wide summit area of High Street (828m) acted as a snow

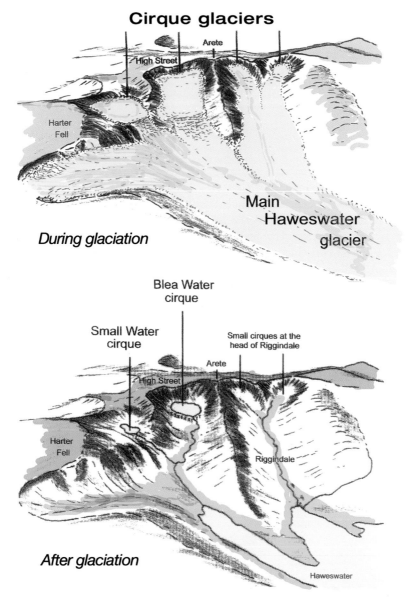

Figure 24 High Street Cirques.

gathering ground. The glacier in the NE facing hollow of Blea Water had almost optimum shade conditions maximising its preservation and its ability to excavate an almost perfect deep round basin. The tarn is exceptionally deep (63m) for its area. An arcuate band of morainic debris up to 25m thick lies along the rocky lip. The less well developed cirque containing Small Water and the two smaller cirque basins at the head of neighbouring Riggindale are separated from the Blea Water cirque by arête ridges.

An extensive research literature exists on Lakeland cirques. They clearly vary in size and shape, some are 'well developed' and show classic features, whereas others are deemed 'indistinct', 'marginal' or 'dubious' depending on the expert you consult. Many are clustered together into groups in various ways. Most authorities list just over 200 cirque basins in the Lake District fells. Figure 25 shows the distribution of around 150 of the best examples.

Altitude, aspect and geology control the distribution. Cirques are found in all the highest mountain blocks (those with summits over 720m), but in the west, cirques also exist on some of the lower fells, for example on Black Combe, Kinninside and the Loweswater Fells all below 600m (Figure 25). This reinforces what we have seen already with regard to the glacial troughs, that is, erosive ice was effective down to lower altitudes in the west and south-west of the district. Cirque basins on the eastern Helvellyn and High Street fells are amongst the highest in the district.

Most cirques are on slopes facing N or E. This has already been illustrated by the High Street cirques, but is also well seen with the classic features on the east side of the Helvellyn ridge, the cirques of the Coniston fells or those on the Red Pike/High Stile/High Crag ridge above Buttermere (Front Cover). As Figure 25 shows however, there are several cirques developed in less favourable aspects.

Whatever way you count cirques in the Lake District the majority (over 80%) are to be found on rocks of the Borrowdale Volcanic Group. To some extent this is due to the fact that these resistant materials dominate Central Lakeland and form much of the highest ground. A significant factor however, is that the nature and variation within these volcanic rocks (thick lavas, bedded volcanic ashes and complex pyroclastics) enables them to be selectively eroded by glacial ice and to be particularly conducive to glacial plucking and scouring and able to retain the imprint of glacial erosion. There are a few cirques developed on the granites of Buttermere/Ennerdale and of Eskdale in the west; rocks which respond to glacial erosion in a similar way to the volcanics. Over the extensive outcrop of the Skiddaw Group rocks on the high ground of the NW an N fells however, the relative ease by which these dominantly slatey rocks break down seems to impede cirque development. Fewer than around 20 good cirques can be seen in these fells.

Overall relatively few Lakeland cirques hold tarns. 19 good examples of cirque tarns in well developed cirque basins exist, with several others holding peat bogs that may have once been tarns.

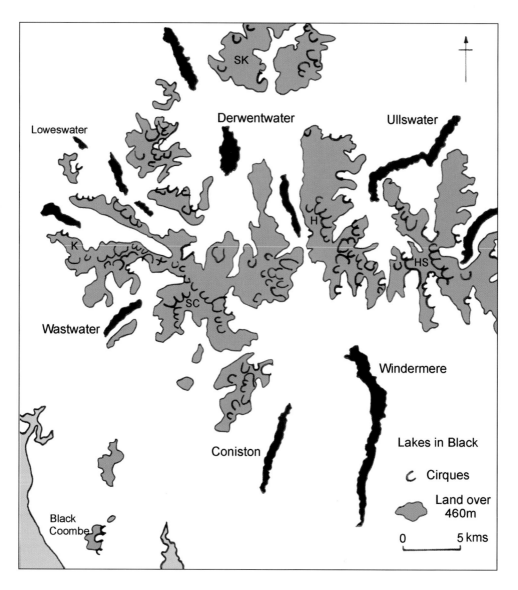

Figure 25 Glacial Cirques in the Lake District.

(SK Skiddaw, K Kinninside, SC Scafell, H Helvellyn, HS High Street)

Figure 26 (above)
The Blea Water cirque – view is looking north westwards from the summit of Harter Fell.

Figure 27 (left)
The arête of Striding Edge on Helvellyn between the cirque basins of Red Tarn to the left and Nethermost Cove to the right.

Figure 28 (below)
The classic cirque basin of Angle Tarn seen from the summit of Bow Fell. The tarn (16m deep) is almost circular in outline and fills the floor of the cirque.

THE LOWLANDS

The rock material scoured by ice from the Lakeland Fells now lies thick over the surrounding lowlands and blankets much of the floor of the northern Irish Sea. The rock debris, much of it ground down to sand and clay, was plastered over the Vale of Eden, the Solway Lowlands, the plains of West Cumbria and the low ground of the Furness and Morecambe Bay peninsulas. Predominantly it is **glacial till**, a heavily compacted clay with embedded pebbles and boulders, which the ice pressed hard on to the lowland terrain. The more descriptive term **boulder clay** is often used to describe this till. Mixed with it are spreads of **glacial sands** and **gravels** flushed out by the meltwaters generated as the ice decayed and down wasted as a spent force abandoned on the low ground. Initially, drainage was impeded and uncoordinated over these lowlands as they emerged from beneath the wasting ice. Depressions filled with water and hollows collected peat. River systems progressively cut into this debris moving and redistributing it.

Figure 29 (left above) Bedded glacial sands and gravels exposed in the coastal cliffs at Gutterby on the SW coast of Cumbria and (right) typical boulder clay – here at Selker Point near Bootle on the Cumbria coast. The deposit consists of pebbles and boulders of Eskdale Granite and Borrowdale Volcanic rocks in a reddish clay matrix. (The hammer is 28cms long).

Figure 30 shows the present day extent of all these superficial materials (boulder clay, glacial sands and gravels, modern alluvial deposits and peat) over the Lakeland region. Almost everywhere in lowland Cumbria the bedrock is not seen. Glacial and other deposits lie tens or even hundreds of metres thick over the lowlands. In contrast the bare ice eroded rocky Lakeland fells stand proud.

Figure 30
Superficial deposits over the Lakeland region. (Shaded areas)

Much of the boulder clay lodged on to the Cumbrian lowlands was shaped up by the moving ice into **drumlins** – smooth, oval-shaped or elliptical hills orientated with the direction of flow of the ice. They are usually between 5 and 50m high and 10-1000m long, with a steeper, blunter end pointing in the up-ice direction and a more gentle streamlined profile at the lower end. They occur in distinct groups which are usually referred to as 'fields' or 'swarms'. Lakeland has some of the best drumlin swarms of any region of Britain. Much of the Eden Valley, the Solway Plain and the lowlands of West Cumbria, and the valley floors of Low Furness and SE Cumbria are covered with drumlin forms, in total probably several thousand of these distinctive hillocks.

The shape and orientation of drumlins tells us a great deal about the nature and behaviour of ice over the lowlands. The fact that they have a steeper blunt end pointing towards the flow direction is similar to the design of aircraft wings. This is an efficient shape. The greater the elongation in the cross-sectional shape of a wing, the greater the air speed it can withstand. In a similar way birds' eggs have a streamlined form. A birds' egg is usually laid blunt end first, the pressure there is greatest. Birds that lay large eggs relative to their size (eg Bitterns) tend to lay the most elongated eggs, whereas birds with relatively small eggs tend to be more rounded (eg Golden Plover). By analogy drumlins formed under slowly moving ice are more rounded, whereas under faster ice they are streamlined out into longer shapes.

Figure 31 Drumlin field around Crooklands, south east of Kendal. (Close to Junction 36 on the M6 Motorway, which is seen at the left) The view is looking northwards from Farleton Fell.

Limit of Drumlin
Upper end

Direction of ice flow

Lower end

Figure 32 A drumlin at Gleaston in Low Furness nicely defined by the hedgeline along its base and by the field boundaries curving over its crest.

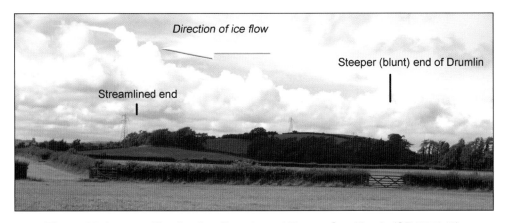

Figure 33 Long profile of a drumlin at Lane Hill near Crooklands (SD 527843). The length: width ratio here is approximately 3:1.

A simple way of measuring drumlins is to compare their length to their width. On average most drumlins have a length to width ratio of around **3:1** (i.e. they are 3 times longer than they are wide). Detailed measurements of the hundreds of drumlins in the Eden Valley and Solway Lowlands show that in the head of the Eden Valley, above Appleby, the length to width ratio is **2.5:1** indicating relatively slowly moving ice and moreover an orientation showing ice moving up-valley escaping SE over the Stainmore Gap across the Pennines. By contrast lower down the Eden Valley in the vicinity of Penrith the ratio is just over **3:1** and the ice is going northwards. Even further down valley around Carlisle the ratio drops to **1.9:1** where ice must have been congested and affected by ice coming down from Scotland. Further west in the neighbourhood of Wigton and Aspatria on the Solway Plain the ratios are as high as **4.6:1** indicating fast and freely moving ice streaming westwards out towards the Irish Sea.

STAGNANT ICE

Ice was not always moving over the lowlands. At times, particularly in the final stages of a glacial, ice sheets broke up and thick patches became stranded and simply stagnated, gradually thinning and wasting away. This was the case for example, over much of the lowland fringe of W. Lakeland, where ice in the late stages of the Devensian was pushed on to the low coastal areas from the Irish Sea and abandoned. Debris contained in the ice simply melted out and was dumped on to the landscape leaving behind a chaotic, irregular terrain. Often huge rafts of ice were buried in the debris, eventually melting out slowly, leading to subsidence of the debris surface and the creation of depressions or **kettle holes.** Many of these now hold sizeable tarns, for example Martin Tarn, near Wigton (NY 258515) or Tarn Dubbs just inland of the coast at Mawbray (NY 115475). On the coastal strip south of St Bees around Nethertown (NX 996075) and Braystones (NX 004060) there is a belt of classic kettle hole terrain with a host of smaller tarns, irregular pits and small ponds between mounds of glacial debris. On the same stretch of coast Barfield Tarn (Figure 34) is a further classic kettle hole.

Figure 34
Barfield Tarn,
S. of Bootle.
A large shallow kettle
hole tarn.

Figure 35
Tarn Moss, Troutbeck,
West of Penrith
(NY 400275).
An infilled kettle hole now
an important National
Nature Reserve with a
protected wetland fauna
and flora.

Figure 36
Typical terrain of stagnant
ice – small depressions,
shallow ponds and low
undulating mounds of
glacial debris.
Rampside in Low Furness
(SD 232664).

MELTWATERS

Once the ice started to melt huge volumes of meltwater were released on to the landscape. Meltwater is a highly dynamic, quick acting and destructive force. Pulled by gravity, water would seek out passageways to the lowest ground, which in Lakeland terms was predominatly out westwards and southwards into the Irish Sea Basin. Water would flow across the top of the ice sheets (**supra-glacial**), through tunnels and passages inside the ice (**en-glacial**) as well as underneath the ice (**sub-glacial**) where it would cut down into whatever it hit in the landsurface below (rock or glacial debris). In extreme cases we know that water under hydrostatic pressure beneath the ice enabled water to flow uphill cutting channels in the landsurface with reversed gradients.

In the present Lakeland landscape it is still possible to see hundreds of these former meltwater or glacial drainage channels. Some lie as open, abandoned, dry channels cut incongruously into the landscape. Others have been occupied by present day streams. Some clearly acted as major conduits for the escaping waters being cut deep into the landscape for long distances and were operational for long periods. The Nannycatch system for example, (NY 056135), east of Cleator Moor is over 4kms long and at its deepest near its northern end, is 90m deep with a steep sided U-shape cross profile, all cut into solid rock. This allowed meltwaters from the Ennerdale Valley to escape southwards and drain into the Calder valley down towards Egremont (Figure 38). Furness Abbey (SD 218716), on the outskirts of Barrow-in-Furness, stands within a meltwater channel of similar proportions. This was a route taken by meltwater southwards across the Low Furness peninsula and now provides a well graded through route for the railway line between Barrow and Dalton. The entrance into Whitehaven from the north by the A 595 from Parton now follows a magnificent 'dry' meltwater feature (NX 979197).

Figure 37 shows a more complex series of features cut by meltwaters along the flanks of the SW Cumbrian fells between Muncaster and Black Coombe. Here, the results of some work done by the author some years ago show how an interconnecting series of channels, mostly cut into the rock under the ice sheet, conveyed meltwaters southwards. Some of the channels (J and K) became major feeder systems. Others were short and isolated (H). In some cases (A-D) they represent a situation where meltwaters en-glacially just happened to cut down and by chance nick into the ridge top of Muncaster Fell. Many of the channels at their lower ends simply fed meltwater back into the ice sheet – hence as we see them now in the present landscape, they evidently seem to end with no obvious continuation (L, and Y for example).

Many other areas of Lakeland still retain similar networks of meltwater channels – particularly the Eden Valley and around the edges of the fells where the break of slope between the high ground and the lowlands caused a concentration of meltwaters (for example the systems of channels that cut the limestone area of Aughertree Fell, near Caldbeck (NY 260385).

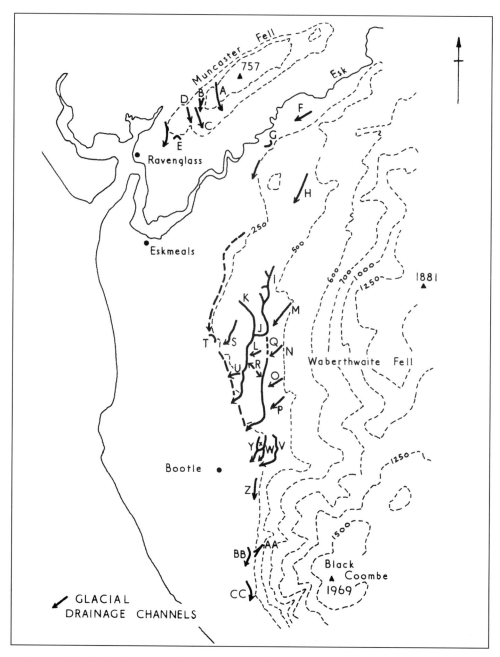

Figure 37 Glacial Drainage Channels in SW Cumbria. The channels are labelled A-Z and then AA-CC. The contours and spot heights are in feet. Channel T is shown with a broken line as only one side of the feature remains.

Figure 38
The Nannycatch Channel.
View looking down the
valley in the direction of
meltwater flow.

Figure 39
Damkirk Channel.
V on Figure 37.

Figure 40
Bootle Fell Channel.
W on Figure 37.

THE FINAL STAGES

Climate ameliorated quite rapidly at the end of the Devensian glacial. Whereas the great ice dome took perhaps 30,000 years or more to build up, it wasted away in little more than 5,000 years. Deglaciation was achieved largely by in situ melting and gradual thinning of the ice. Much of the high ground probably became ice free before the valleys and lowlands. Glaciers in the main valley troughs wasted back into the central mountains. In some of the valleys today stadial moraines exist marking points where the main glaciers paused and stood still for long enough to allow debris to melt out and accumulate at their snouts as **terminal moraines**. Examples occur at Haverthwaite in the Rusland valley, at the southern end of Windermere near Newby Bridge and at the end of Coniston at Nibthwaite. The last places to retain ice were the high shaded cirque basins.

As the Lakeland landscape emerged from beneath the ice cover a different set of landform processes gradually took over. Melting of the ice had a distinctly seasonal pattern. Large quantities of broken down rock material, boulders, sand and finer debris was washed down from the bare slopes in the summers into the valley floors. At first **periglacial** processes continued to be active in the winters, breaking down exposed rock and moving material by **solifluction** processes on slopes. Water swiftly occupied the deep ice scoured rock basins to create the major lakes such as Wastwater and Ullswater, but in many of the other valleys temporary shallow lakes must have existed. Gradually however the shallower valley floors were overwhelmed with debris washing from the slopes and the temporary lakes were infilled. This process is well seen in such places as Great Langdale, one of the main Lakeland glacial troughs no longer retaining a major lake. A very important progressive change was the colonisation of the landscape by vegetation, the principal effect of which was the stabilisation of slopes and a reduction in the supply of loose debris to the valley floors and lake basins.

A record of these changing events can be picked up in the pattern of sediments that collected in the valley floors and more particularly at the bottom of the lakes and tarns. A considerable amount of pioneering research work in this field has centred on Cumbrian lakes and tarns and has provided not only data on this immediate post-glacial period for Lakeland, but also type sites for the whole of the British timescale. It was cores taken from the floor of Windermere and other Lakeland tarns that enabled the **Windermere Interstadial** to be first identified and dated. Additionally, data assembled from lake and tarn cores helped decipher the succeeding **Loch Lomond Stadial** and events in the more recent post-glacial **Flandrian** period. (Figure 2). The record in the sediments shows at first thick deposits of debris with no organic material at all, the product of rapid downwashing from an unvegetated landscape. The material is often distinctly laminated in seasonal accumulations showing summer melting and retarded supply in the winters. Above these, as conditions began to ameliorate, vegetation debris, pollen grains and animal remains are found and are capable of being dated and related to environmental conditions appertaining at the time of deposition. The methods involved in this work are beyond the scope of this booklet, but they have enabled a good picture of Lakeland at this period to be reconstructed.

In the early part of the **Windermere Interstadial** (around 13,000 years ago) tundra conditions still existed in Lakeland. The mean July temperature has been estimated to have been around 14°C. Figures like this have been derived principally by studying beetle remains in sediments; beetles are particularly sensitive to temperature and inhabit very specialised environmental niches. The ice had gone completely from the Lakeland fells as lake sediments ceased to show ice melt deposits. Winters were still cold at altitude, but vegetation was just beginning to take a hold. The record of pollen grains recovered suggests limited vegetation, a largely treeless tundra with rates of pollen influx very low. By 12,550 years ago the mean July temperature had risen to around 15°C (a figure close to the present day mean). As the interstadial progressed pollen rates increase but variations in the plant cover are clearly discernable between upland and lowland. The lowlands supported birch woodland and could possibly have been capable of sustaining nomadic human life but there is no evidence for it in Cumbria.

THE LOCH LOMOND STADIAL

The record of sediments on the lake floors shows a major deterioration of climate and the return to glacial and severe periglacial conditions between approximately 11-10,000 years BP. This phase is named from W. Scotland where similar but slightly more severe conditions prevailed, but there, as in Wales and Lakeland (Figure 4) the highest mountains saw the reappearance of ice. The mean July temperature for the period has been calculated to have dropped below 8°C. Cirques in Lakeland developed in the Devensian glacial were re-occupied by ice. Perennial snow beds existed down to altitudes around 300m. Most obvious today in the landscape are the moraines, mound like deposits and spreads of debris that still lie fresh where these small glaciers lay. Over 70 separate locations have now been identified where these Loch Lomond phase glaciers built up (Figure 41). The best examples are at the head of the Langdale (Figure 43) and Borrowdale valleys (Figure 44), or in Upper Ennerdale around the Black Sail YHA. An easily seen series of these moraines are those on the western roadside of the A591 as the ascent is made out of Grasmere, going up on to Dunmail Raise (NY 328110). Detailed examination of the morainic landforms and debris left behind is still going on. Work seems to suggest that winds during the period came dominantly from a southerly direction and that the central part of the east-west axis of the Lakeland fells received the heaviest snowfalls. Most of the highest cirques and valley heads were re-occupied by small glaciers from Black Coombe in the south to the Skiddaw Fells in the north. Recent research work has posed the possibility that a more extensive plateau ice field may have existed at this time over parts of the central fells, notably over the area centred on High Raise and Thunacar Knott between Borrowdale and Langdale (NY 281095) (Figure 42). Smaller plateau icefields may also have built up centred on the Grey Knotts/Brandreth/Honister area (NY 220125).

Relatively thin ice may have collected on these plateau tops and was probably quite protective with minimal impact on the form of the summit areas. However, tongues of ice may have descended into the valleys. Very detailed mapping of the moraines and debris left behind suggests ice could, for example, have extended some distance down into

Borrowdale, into the Wythburn Valley towards Thirlmere and down to Stickle Tarn in the Langdale Pikes. Within Borrowdale there are a series of curved terminal moraines across the valley floor at Rosthwaite that have been much studied and still remain rather a puzzle. They may in fact relate to a tongue of this Loch Lomond phase ice from the High Raise field (Figure 42). Previous interpretations have suggested they are stillstand positions of main Devensian valley glaciers. Lateral moraines on the lower valley sides of the Langstrath, Stonethwaite and Upper Borrowdale valleys (shown diagrammatically on Figure 42) may also relate to this Loch Lomond phase.

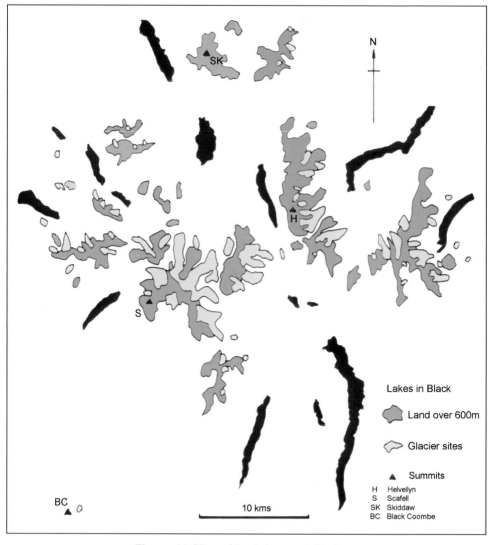

Figure 41 Sites of Loch Lomond Glaciers

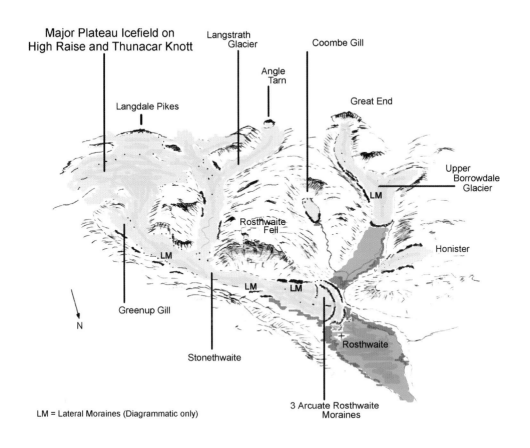

Major Plateau Icefield on High Raise and Thunacar Knott

Langstrath Glacier

Coombe Gill

Angle Tarn

Langdale Pikes

Great End

Upper Borrowdale Glacier

LM

Rosthwaite Fell

Honister

LM

LM   LM

Greenup Gill

N

Rosthwaite

Stonethwaite

LM = Lateral Moraines (Diagrammatic only)

3 Arcuate Rosthwaite Moraines

Figure 42
Suggested Loch Lomond Stadial Plateau Icefield and glacier tongues
in the Langstrath, Stonethwaite and Rosthwaite areas.

The Loch Lomond glaciers were short lived. The cold period as a whole lasted little over a 1000 years. Ice would have taken several hundred years to build up and may well have been active for perhaps only half of this period. It clearly melted away from most locations in situ, leaving behind an array of humps, mounds and ridges in these locations (Figures 43-47)

Once the Loch Lomond ice finally disappeared around about 10,000 BP the ice age in Lakeland was over. We entered the **Flandrian**, the true post-glacial, the present period of geological time. In reality it is probably just another interglacial - unless of course man-made global warming turns out to be a decisive new phase in earth history.

Figure 43
Group of Loch Lomond
morainic mounds at the
head of the Langdale
Valley (centre of photo).

Figure 44
Loch Lomond lateral
moraines in Upper
Borrowdale, just below
Stockley Bridge.
(NY 235114) looking
up valley.

Figure 45
Loch Lomond
moraines below
Easedale Tarn.

Figure 46 The terminal moraine at Rosthwaite. The picture shows the middle one of the three moraines. It now forms no more than a low bracken covered ridge stretching across the enclosed fields on the valley floor.

Figure 47 Section in the outer Rosthwaite moraine where the River Derwent has cut through the moraine ridge. Close to Longthwaite YHA.

PERIGLACIATION

Periglaciation literally means 'round about' or 'near' glaciation. Close to any ice sheet or glacier there is always a zone, the periglacial zone, which experiences prolonged exposure to intensely cold but non-glacial conditions. In the Northern Hemisphere at the present day for example, there are huge areas surrounding the Arctic ice caps and in the very highest mountains where periglacial conditions prevail. Permafrost penetrates deep into the ground and exposed rock and mountain tops are subjected to severe weathering under sub zero temperatures. The extent of periglacial conditions thus varies in both space and time.

In the Lake District, even during the glacials, we have seen that perhaps not all the ground was covered by ice all of the time. The ice-free areas would however have been under periglacial conditions. During the interglacial after the main Devensian ice had wasted away, the high fells may well have had long periods of intense cold. The Loch Lomond Stadial brought the ice back to some of the highest parts of Lakeland but again, surrounding areas must have been subjected to frost processes. At the present time the Lakeland fells are not high enough to retain anything like permafrost, let alone permanent ice, but environmental conditions present a distinctive maritime periglacial regime. Conditions on the high fell tops are of high humidity, intense precipitation, strong blustery winds and significant winter snow cover. Extreme sub zero temperatures are not a feature, but 30-40 freezing cycles per year with frost in the ground in up to 6 of the winter months occur. Snow can also lie in the highest mountain parts for over 50 days a year.

The periglacial landforms in the Lake District today may therefore, be 'relict' dating back to the Devensian and late glacial, or alternatively we can demonstrate that processes are still 'active' on the highest mountain tops. A wide range of landform features, deposits and sedimentary structures ascribed to periglacial processes have been identified in the district. Intense weathering of bedrock at high altitude leads to break down of rock and the production of loose rock debris that may now lie on fellside ridges as **blockfields** (Figure 15) or on slopes as aprons of scree or cones of debris. More subtle effects are seen in small scale **patterned ground**, where regular arrangement of stones by freezing and thawing produces **stone stripes** or **polygons**. Complex differential frost heaving can create hummock structures and **thurfur** mounds. Downslope movement of soil and debris subjected to seasonal freezing and thawing produces a range of micro slope features including **solifluction lobes**, **turf bank terraces** and **ploughing blocks**.

Figure 48 Thurfur mounds on Great Dun Fell in Eastern Lakeland (NY710320).

Figure 49
Active Periglacial Stone Stripes at approx 640m on High Pike (NY319350). The lines of coarse stones running down the slope (Top right to bottom left) are approx 45cms apart. Between are bands of finer material. The rock is Skiddaw Group slate. The camera lens cap in the centre of the picture is 6cms in diameter.

Figure 50
Active turf bank terraces on the summit plateau of Robinson (NY 203168) The lines of two of the terraces are shown by the dotted lines. Person standing on the summit cairn gives the scale.

Figure 51
Ploughing Blocks at 650m on the northern slopes of Seat Sandal (NY 343117) Two large blocks of volcanic rock have moved downslope associated with solifluction processes. Note the furrow created above the blocks and the 'bow wave' feature in the turf pushed up below the blocks. In both figures 48 and 51 the folded OS map near the centres of the pictures gives the scale.

49

LIMESTONE PAVEMENTS

Limestone pavements are one of Britain's rarest and most distinctive landscape features. These huge sweeping surfaces of bare limestone rock are criss-crossed with deep fissures (**grikes**) etched out along the natural joints in the rock, with pitted and grooved blocks (**clints**) between. In total there are only about 3,000 hectares of pavement in Britain but around 40% lie in Lakeland. Without the ice age these features would never have developed.

Figure 52 Gently dipping limestone pavement on Holme Fell (SD 5479) east of Kendal. Bare runneled pavement surfaces with scattered limestone blocks and glacial erratics.

A number of special requirements come together in Lakeland to produce these features. Mechanically strong and relatively pure beds of Carboniferous limestone lying in thick, horizontal or slightly dipping sheets encircle the central Lakeland fells from Cockermouth in the north down over the Westmorland fells on the eastern side and then round the south of the district to the Lakeland peninsulas around Morecambe Bay. Most importantly these rocks were swept across and scoured by the ice moving away from the high Lakeland Fells. The overburden of weathered and broken rock near the surface was stripped away by moving ice, revealing large areas of fresh limestone outcrop. In many places the ice left behind thin covers of glacial tills and wind blown sands (**loess**) on which soils and vegetation developed, as well as scatters of larger erratic boulders. Over the last 10,000 years since the ice has disappeared acidulated rain and ground water percolating through this layer of glacial debris, soil and vegetation has been gently dissolving away the limestone beneath. In many places the thin glacial materials and soils have been gradually washed off the limestone surfaces revealing the intricate pattern of runnels, channels, solution cups, pans and pits. Only the large stranded erratics remain reminding us of the significant part played by the ice.

Figure 53 Stranded glacial erratics on limestone pavements.
(Left) a boulder of Borrowdale Volcanic rock on limestone at Knipe Scar (NY 5219) –
rucksack to left for scale. (Right) a much larger split erratic boulder of Silurian gritstone
on Lords Seat, the limestone summit of Whitbarrow (SD 4488).

Figure 54 Loess deposits on Farleton Knott (SD 5480) Short limestone grassland
with bare limestone surfaces and loose scree on left. Below and to the right the taller mat
grass (Nardus stricta) and gorse picks out the loess. This is a buff coloured wind blown silt
winnowed from glacial outwash sediments left by the melting glaciers in the Late Devensian.

The finest pavement areas are on Knipe Scar (S. of Penrith), the Orton Fells and Great
Asby Scar in the east, Farleton Knott, Holme Fell and Hutton Roof (E. of Kendal) and
Gaitbarrows, Whitbarrow and Urswick in the Morecambe Bay area. Many of these areas
have protected status because of the fragility of these unique environments, but they are
well documented with many explanatory leaflets and guides.

CHANGING SEA LEVELS

Ice ages impact directly and very dramatically on sea levels. Two groups of processes are involved. First with the onset of cold conditions increasing amounts of water become locked up in glaciers and ice sheets on the land and hence world-wide sea levels fall. Coastlines extend further and further out and more of the sea bed becomes exposed. When climatic conditions ameliorate and glaciers and ice sheets begin to melt the process is reversed, the sea rises and transgresses back onto the land. These changes are known as **eustatic movements**. They are simple and straight forward to understand but in practice difficult to measure precisely as the capacity of the world's ocean basins is constantly changing as a result of earth movements and changes in the configuration of the continents and coastlines. The process is continuous, the seas rising and falling as climatic conditions oscillate. Large quantities of water are of course still locked up today in ice sheets and glaciers, particularly in Antarctica and Greenland. One of the current concerns over global warming is the impact this will have on rising sea levels.

Superimposed on to this eustatic fluctuation is a more complex process known as **isostatic movement**. As glaciers and ice sheets build up on the landmasses their weight depresses the earths crust. The crust responds rather like a rubber sheet floating on water. The crust is most heavily depressed beneath the large ice masses and less so where ice accumulation is less. The crust is thus distorted into a series of complex swells and depressions. Once the ice melts and the burden of ice on the crust is relieved it bounces back (rebounds) quite quickly at first, but the rate of readjustment slows down and can take very long periods to regain original levels. In fact isostatic rebound is still going on today in Britain, over 10,000 years since the ice disappeared.

The net effect of these two processes produces changes in the relative levels of the land and the sea. Most estimates show that round about the Last Glacial Maximum sea levels worldwide had fallen at least 120m. Under these conditions much of the southern North Sea and the English Channel were land and there was probably a land bridge in the S.Irish Sea between Wales and Ireland. However by about 17,000 to 14,000 years BP, during the deglaciation, sea levels in the Irish Sea stood above present mean sea level. By how much is disputed, but most reasonable estimates put it to 10-15 above present levels.

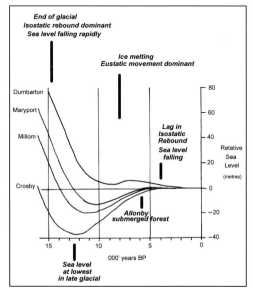

Figure 55
Sea Level Curves for eastern Irish Sea.

The main reason for this high relative level was isostatic depression. Isostatic rebound quickly took over however, resulting in very rapid sea level falls as the land moved upwards (Figure 55). As rebound slowed the effects of the eustatic rise began to dominate and hence sea levels rose.

Figure 56 illustrates that because isostatic depression in Britain was dominated by the massive weight of ice over the W. Highlands of Scotland the pattern of rebound has a broad north-south component. Cumbria lies close to the transition point between the heavily depressed crust over Scotland to the north and the slightly elevated bulge upwards over England and Wales. Consequently as the map shows, a very slight rise in the land relative to the sea has been going on in Cumbria and northwards into Scotland whereas from approximately Merseyside southwards the land has been sinking. The relative sea level curves in Figure 55 show the differences along the Irish Sea coast between Crosby (in Merseyside just north of Liverpool), Millom on the SW Cumbria coast on the Duddon estuary, Maryport in W. Cumbria close to the mouth of the Solway Firth and then at Dumbarton on the Clyde coast of Scotland.

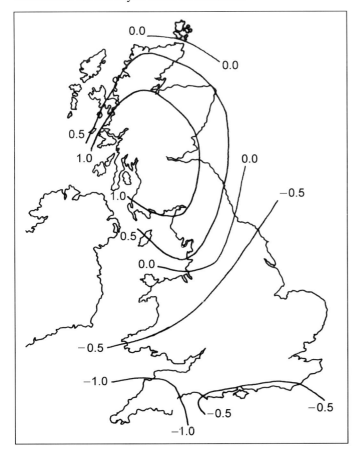

Figure 56
Rates of relative sea level change over the last 4000 years (mm/year). The positive values over N.England and Scotland indicate relative sea level fall or land uplift. Lakeland has thus been gently rising. The negative value over S.Britain indicate relative sea level rise or land subsidence.

The Cumbria coast is not an ideal site to illustrate sea level changes in a simple way. With the exception of the short rocky coastline around Whitehaven and St. Bees and the rocky limestone peninsulas running south into Morecambe Bay most of the coastline is formed of unconsolidated glacial materials which has been constantly eroded and cliffed by present day wave action thus destroying any possible records of different sea level positions. Three areas however do illustrate the effects of sea level change.

On both sides of the Solway Firth a series of 'raised beaches' have been identified and related to high sea level positions around about 6,500 years BP. Whilst not as dramatic as the sharp platforms cut into solid rock around the coasts of the highlands and islands of Scotland they are relicts of former higher sea levels. (Figure 57) The highest level mapped as the **second terrace** lies at approximately 7m (23ft) in the west rising to 8.3m (27ft) at the head of the estuary. The lower feature (**first terrace**) is at 5.5m (18ft) in the west and at 6.5m (21ft) further east. Below these lie the modern beaches.

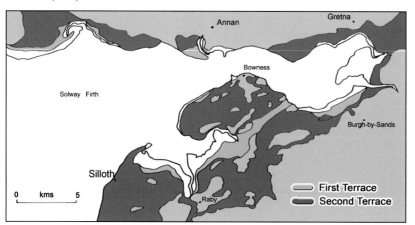

Figure 57
The Raised Beaches around the Solway Firth.

Around Morecambe Bay the coastline is very different with steep-sided limestone peninsulas projecting southwards into the bay and standing above large expanses of low lying land along the estuaries (Figure 58). Glaciers clearly overrode the limestone hills and scoured the estuaries to rock head well below present sea levels. With the melting of the ice and the flooding back of the sea into these estuaries, marine sands and silts driven in from the sea, combined with river alluvium brought down from the land, caused extensive deposition of sediments. The limestone hills must at times have marked the coastline but now are some distance inland. For many years it was argued that along the flanks of these limestone hills wave-cut notches, marine benches and sea caves could be cited as direct evidence of former high sea levels. The Grand Arch, a cave at 34m above present sea level and a possible blow-hole feature on the western side of Humphrey Head was held as a particular example of a marine feature. Recent work however has destroyed this thesis by demonstrating they are much older features in the erosional history of the limestone. The point remains however that the coastline once lay along the flanks of these limestone hills and the infill of the estuaries must be related to sea level changes following deglaciation.

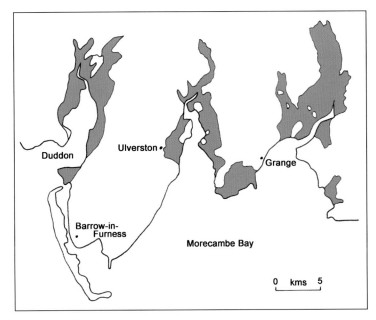

Figure 58
The infilled
estuaries of
South Lakeland.

There are a number of sites on the Cumbrian coast where '**submerged forests**' occur. The clearest example is at Allonby (SD 084484) where there are stumps of trees and abundant pieces of trunks and branches exposed on the foreshore at low tide in a position far below where they must have originally grown. At other points such as Drigg (SD 047985) and Tarn Bay (SD 079909) debris and organic remains can also be seen below present high tide levels. Expert interpretation of all these sites has as yet failed to pin down all of these deposits to very precise former sea levels, but again there can be no doubt they illustrate changing relative levels of land and sea related to ice-age events and the subsequent re-adjustments in the last 10,000 years. (Figure 59 and back cover).

Figure 59
Tree stump
exposed on the
foreshore
submerged forest
at Allonby.
This and most of
the exposed
stumps are oaks
and they date
from approximately
6,500 years BP.

PARAGLACIATION

Long after all the ice melted away and the meltwaters were dispersed, the effects of ice on the Lake District were still being felt. In the last section we have seen that ice ages had a profound effect on the relative levels of the land and the sea, adjustments that take very long periods to be resolved. The failure of rock slopes was another long term consequence of the glaciation.

Glacial erosion within Lakeland, particularly in the core area of the high fells, caused steepening of rockwalls and valley deepening, leading in some cases to the weakening of the foundations of large rock exposures. The weight of ice also imposes stresses on the valley floors and sides. Once the ice had gone the loss of ice support can result in stress release as the rock masses experience unloading and rebound. Such rock slope failures are termed **paraglacial** (glacially-conditioned) phenomena.

Research work in the last five years has identified up to 40 sites in the Lake District where rock slope failure has resulted in landslips and rockfalls of various kinds which can be related to paraglacial effects. Dating such features is very difficult. Many may well have occurred almost immediately after the burden of the Devensian ice on the landscape was relieved. Others can be shown to be related to the later Loch Lomond Readvance Glaciation and a few can be pinned down by historical data to more recent times right up into the 20th Century – for example major rock falls and slope failures on Doves Nest Crag on the trough walls of Coombe Gill, Borrowdale (NY 254117). The form of these features varies widely according to the geological circumstances. Some involve rock masses sliding down as intact bodies of rock. Some involve rock masses rotating as they fall, others result in massive rock falls giving rise to huge sheets of scree (**talus**) debris, or huge detached blocks like the famous Bowder Stone in Borrowdale.

Figure 60
Doves Nest Crag,
Coombe Gill, renewed
movement at this site
occurred in 1978-9.

Figures 61-63 illustrate some examples of these features. Other significant failures have been described on Illgill Head (NY 174057) at the top of the Wastwater Screes, on Helm Crag, Grasmere (NY 328093) where the very unusual shape of the summit is related to rock slope failure and on Crag Fell, Ennerdale (NY 095147).

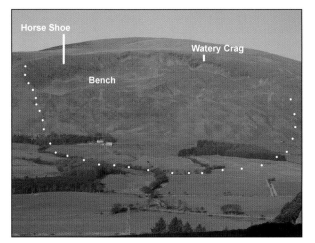

Figure 61
A major rock slope failure in Skiddaw Group mudstone rocks on the south east face of Cotley, Black Combe.(SD 145845) The curved head scarp where failure occurred is marked by Horse Shoe and Watery Crag, beneath is the rotationally slipped bench of Rabbit Crags. The extent of the failure debris is shown by the dotted line.

Figure 62
View down slope of the Antiscarps on the north facing slope at the eastern end of Clough Head over looking Threlkeld. (NY 336232). A series of 2m high scarps and 5m wide bench features run along the slope at the base of the screes for up to 350m. They are small slip features in the Skiddaw Group mudstone rocks resulting from paraglacial failure of the slope.

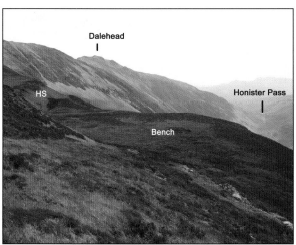

Figure 63
Littledale Edge and Hackney Holes, Robinson (NY 205160). This is the largest paraglacial rock slope failure in the Lake District extending over 1.7 km² of the southern face of Robinson overlooking the Honister Pass. Failed rock masses (Skiddaw Group mudstones) have built a series of benches some tilted backwards. Fissures occur along the top of the feature, notably Hackney Holes which is a rock chasm 15-20m deep and 10m wide. HS on the figure is one of the many low head scarps where failure has occurred.

LIFE

It is not known when man first set foot in Lakeland. Compared with other areas of England it is striking how little evidence there is in the region, not only of any finds of human remains or signs of man's activities, but also of remains of major land animals. It is tempting to speculate on the reasons for this. The argument that conditions were so severe throughout the Devensian that human habitation was impossible is a very powerful one. Given the glacialogical evidence we have examined in the preceding pages it is hard to conceive of human existence of any kind with thick ice so dominant for so long. The continued lack of evidence even into the final stages of the Pleistocene – the Upper Palaeolithic of the archaeologists (30,000 - 11,000 years ago) could also be explained by the harshness of environmental conditions. The mountainous core of Lakeland has always been a difficult area to settle, man only slowly and relatively late in modern times gained a real foothold in this region. The lowland and coastal fringes of Lakeland must have presented better prospects however. The paucity of evidence for early man here also could be countered by arguing that the evidence of any early occupation may have been destroyed by the changing nature of the coastal areas with changing sea levels and inundations. Less convincing is the view that perhaps the evidence has yet to be discovered and so far we simply have not looked hard enough or in the right locations.

The best pieces of evidence of human occupation all come from just outside the region, perhaps suggesting that after all Lakeland was perhaps just beyond the limits of early occupation. Finds of objects discarded by hunter-gathering communities are known from south of the region. The most dramatic was the discovery of an elk skeleton, wounded by barbed arrows, that died in a shallow lake at High Furlong, Poulton-le-Fylde, albeit 40 kms from Lakeland. It yielded a 14C determination of approx 10,250 years. The Victoria Caves in the limestone at Settle in North Yorkshire have similarly yielded good dated stone tools, antler harpoons and animal remains from the late-glacial but sufficiently far from Lakeland to draw firm conclusions of conditions in our region.

Within Lakeland, two sites, Lindale Low Caves (SD 417801) and Kirkhead Cave (SD 391756) both in the limestone near Grange-over-Sands have been subjected to a considerable amount of investigation. Both have yielded tools of flint and antler bone with Palaeolithic characteristics but their dating and provenance has proved debatable.

Evidence for later Mesolithic settlement on the Cumbrian lowlands is strong and well documented, particularly around Eskmeals and at Ehenside Tarn, for example, but perhaps man was not around in ice-age Lakeland.

GLOSSARY OF TERMS USED IN TEXT

Abrasion:

The scraping off or wearing down of rock material – by glaciers for example.

Blockfield:

Spreads of frost-riven boulders, usually on high mountain tops, with little or no vegetation cover.

Borrowdale Volcanic Group:

The principal Group of volcanic rocks that form most of the central fells of the Lake District. They consist of thick beds of lava as well as bedded and broken volcanic debris. They date from the mid-Ordovician period of geological time and are approximately 450 million years old. They are generally resistant and impermeable materials and are particularly susceptible to glacial plucking.

Insolation:

The intensity of solar radiation received on the surface of the ground.

Interglacial / interstadial:

Interglacial refers to a period of warmer climate separating glacial phases. Interstadial is a pause in the advance of a glacier or ice sheet.

Loess:

Accumulations of wind blown particles – in a glacial environment derived from vegetation free areas around ice sheets. The material has a small particle size and is usually unstratified.

Nunatak:

An Eskimo term meaning a rock mass that projects through an ice sheet.

Oxygen Isotope Cycles:

Cyclical variations in the ratio of the masses of oxygen of atomic weights 18 and 16 present in calcite of the ocean floors. The ratio is linked to water temperatures of ancient oceans.

Solifluction:

The slow downhill movement of soil and loose debris on slopes as a result of freezing and thawing processes.

Skiddaw Group Rocks:

The oldest Group of Lakeland rocks dating from the early Ordovician and late Cambrian periods (more than 460 million years old). They are metamorphically altered, deep water sediments and are now mostly hard mudstones, siltstones and slatey materials. Typically they break down into flat, platy fragments.

ACKNOWLEDGEMENTS

All of the photographs are by the author. All the maps and diagrams have been drawn by the author especially for this booklet. The very extensive research literature on Lakeland has been drawn upon for some of the material. It is not possible in a booklet of this kind to acknowledge all the sources individually. Particular acknowledgements are due to Dr I. S. Evans (University of Durham) for some of the data on cirques (Figure 25) and to Dr. Peter Wilson (University of Ulster) for some of the material on paraglaciation. I have also drawn on specific published material by J. B. Sissons, D. A. McDougall, A. L. Lamb, C. K. Ballantyne, W. A. Mitchell, A. Plater, I. Shennan, B. Horton, J. E. Gordon, J. Boardman, J. R. Marshall and P. Vincent.

THE AUTHOR

Dr. Alan Smith is now retired from an academic career. He has written several books, papers and guides on Lakeland geology and geomorphology. He is a Past President and former General Secretary of the Cumberland Geological Society. He lives in Keswick.

COVER PHOTOGRAPHS

Front: The High Crag, High Stile, Red Pike ridge, Buttermere, seen from the Gatesgarth valley. North-easterly facing glacial cirques on the side of the main Buttermere glacial trough.

Back:

Left   *upper:* Lateral Loch Lomond Stadial moraines above Seathwaite at the head of the Borrowdale valley. Note the spread of perched blocks on the morainic mounds.

middle: The Seathwaite valley, Upper Borrowdale, looking up valley, the peak of Base Brown in the middle picture. A flat floored glacial trough with the hanging cirque of Gillercombe to the right of Base Brown.

lower: The summit ridge of Haystacks looking east towards Brandreth. An ice scoured summit – typical 'loch and knockan' topography (page 18).

Right   *upper:* Bleaberry Tarn cirque from the summit of High Stile. Crummock Water in the distance.

middle: The submerged forest on the foreshore at Allonby

lower: The Loch Lomond Stadial curved terminal moraine around the foot of High Hole Crag, Keskadale at the head of Newlands Hause.